★

EURYTHMICS

greatest hits

Wise Publications
London/New York/Sydney

Exclusive Distributors:

Music Sales Limited
8/9 Frith Street,
London W1V 5TZ, England.

Music Sales Pty Limited
120 Rothschild Avenue,
Rosebery. NSW 2018.
Australia.

Art direction by Michael Bell Design
Designed by Laurence Stevens
Typeset by Capital Setters

Music Sales' complete catalogue lists thousands of titles and is free from your local music shop,
or direct from Music Sales Limited. Please send a cheque/postal order for £1.50 for postage to:
Music Sales Limited, Newmarket Road, Bury St. Edmunds, Suffolk IP33 3YB.

Your Guarantee of Quality:-

As publishers, we strive to produce every book to the highest commercial standards.

The book has been carefully designed to minimise awkward page turns, and to make playing from it a real pleasure.

Particular care has been given to specifying acid-free, neutral-sized paper which has not been chlorine bleached
but produced with special regard for the environment. Throughout, the printing and binding have been planned
to ensure a sturdy, attractive publication which should give years of enjoyment.

If your copy fails to meet our high standards, please inform us and we will gladly replace it.

Printed in the United Kingdom by
J.B. Offset Printers (Marks Tey) Limited, Marks Tey, Essex.

EURYTHMICS ★

There Must Be An Angel
(Playing With My Heart)
Sisters Are Doin' It For

Who's That Girl?
Right By Your Side
ere Comes The Rain Again

When Tomorrow Comes

Sex Crime (1984)

You Have Placed A Chill I[n]

Thorn In My Side

Don't Ask Me Why

Would I Lie To You?

Miracle Of Love

Sex Crime (1984)
You Have Placed A Chill In My Heart
Thorn In My Side
Don't Ask Me Why

There Must Be An Angel
(Playing With My Heart)
Sisters Are Doin' It For Themselves
It's Alright (Baby's Coming Back)
When Tomorrow Comes

Would I Lie To You?
Miracle Of Love
Angel
Missionary Man
I Need A Man

Angel
(Coming Back)

EURYTHMICS

greatest hits

EURYTHMICS : greatest hits ★

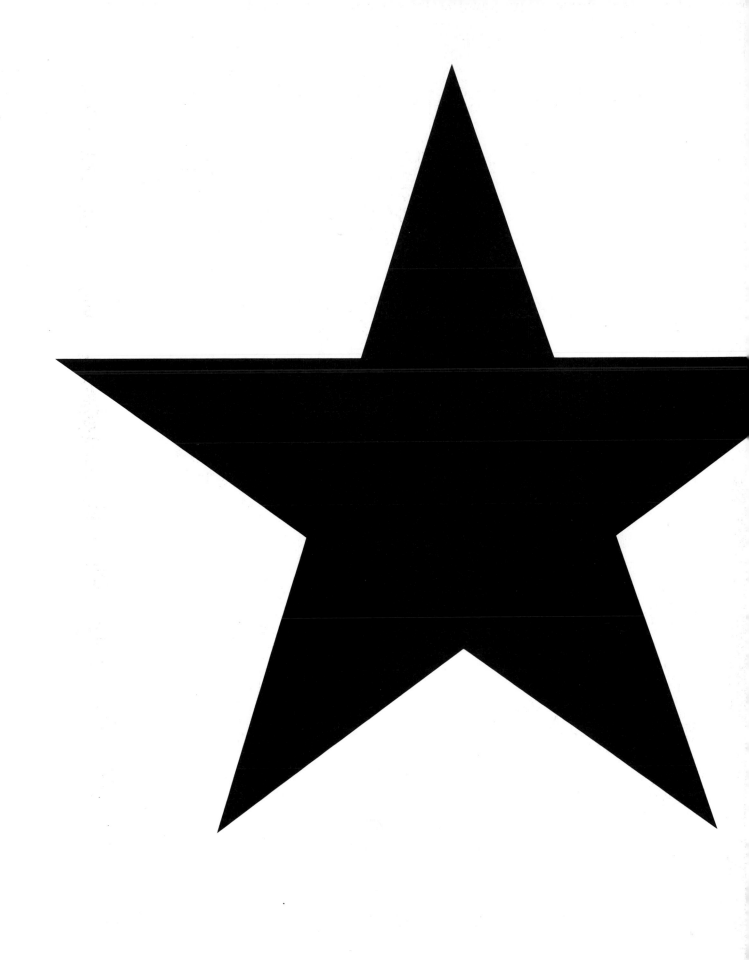

Love Is A Stranger

WORDS & MUSIC BY A. LENNOX & D.A. STEWART

And I want__ you, and I want__ you,

and I want__ you so, it's an ob-ses-sion.

Love is a dan-ger of a diff-'rent kind__ to take you a-way__ and

It's sa-vage and it's cruel and it shines like de-struc-tion, comes in like the flood and it seems like re-li-gion, it's no-ble and it's bru-tal it dis-torts and de-ran-ges and it wren-ches you up___ and you're left___ like a zom-bie.___

And I want___ you,

and I want___ you,   and I want___ you so, it's an ob -

ses-sion.

It's guilt edged, gla-mo-rous and

sleek by de-sign, you know it's jea-lous by na-ture, false and un-kind. It's

Sweet Dreams

WORDS & MUSIC BY D.A. STEWART & A. LENNOX

Sweet dreams are made __ of this, __ who am __ I __ to dis-a-gree? __ I tra-vel the world __ and the sev-en seas, __ ev-'ry-bo-dy's look-ing for some-thing. Some of them want to use __ you,

some of them want to get used — by you,— some of them want to ab-use — you,

some of them want to be — ab - used.—

Hold your head up, keep your head up, mov-in' on. __ Hold your head up, mov-in' on. __

Keep your head up, mov-in' on. __ Hold your head up, mov-in' on. __ Keep your head up, mov-in' on. __

Hold your head up, mov-in' on, __ keep your head up.

Who's That Girl?

WORDS & MUSIC BY A. LENNOX & D.A. STEWART

Who's that___ girl.

The

lang - uage of love___ slips from my lov-er's tongue___ cool-er than ice -
lang - uage of love___ has left me sto-ney grey___ tongue - tied and twist-

cream and warm-er than the sun,___ dumb hearts get brok - en
ed at the price I've had to pay___ your care-less no - tions have

just like chin-a cups.___ The lang-uage of love___ has left me brok-en on the
sil - enced these e - mot-ions. Look at all___ the fool-ish-ness your lov-er's talk___ has done.

Right By Your Side

Words & Music by A. Lennox & D.A. Stewart

24

Here Comes The Rain Again

WORDS & MUSIC BY A. LENNOX & D.A. STEWART

So ba - by

talk to me____   like lov-ers do.____

D.C. to fade

There Must Be An Angel
(Playing With My Heart)

WORDS & MUSIC BY A. LENNOX & D.A. STEWART

CHORUS

Not 2nd time

29

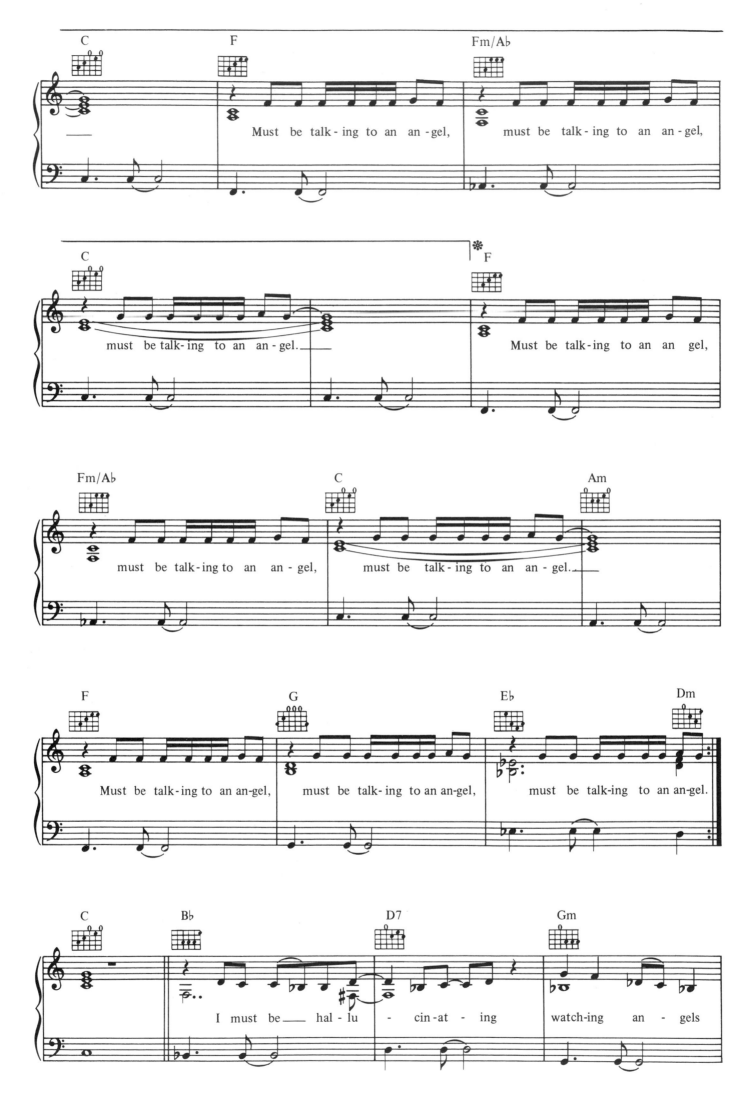

VERSE 2:

No one on earth could feel like this
I'm thrown and over blown with bliss
There must be an angel
Playing with my heart.
And when I think that I'm alone
It seems there's more of us at home
It's a multitude of angels
And they're playing with my heart.

Sisters Are Doin' It For Themselves

WORDS & MUSIC BY A. LENNOX & D.A. STEWART

-en 'cause there's some-thing we for-got to say to you. We say:

Sis - ters are do-in' it for them - selves, stand-in' on their

own two feet and ring-in' on their own bells.

Sis - ters are do-in' it for them - selves. Now, this is a song

to cel - e - brate

the con - scious lib - er - a - tion _____ of the fe -

- male state. _____   Moth - ers, daugh - ters, and.

___ their   daugh - ters, too, _____ yeah, ___

wom - an ___ to   wom - an,   we're   sing - ing with   you. ___

The "in - fe - ri - or sex"   has got a new ex -

- te - ri - or. ___   We got   doc - tors, law - yers, pol -

- i - ti - cians,   too.   Ev -

It's Alright (Baby's Coming Back)

Words & Music by A. Lennox & D.A. Stewart

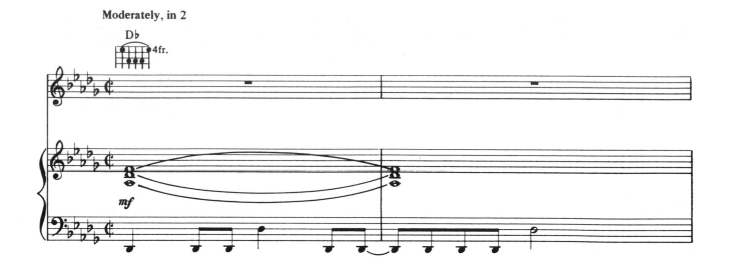

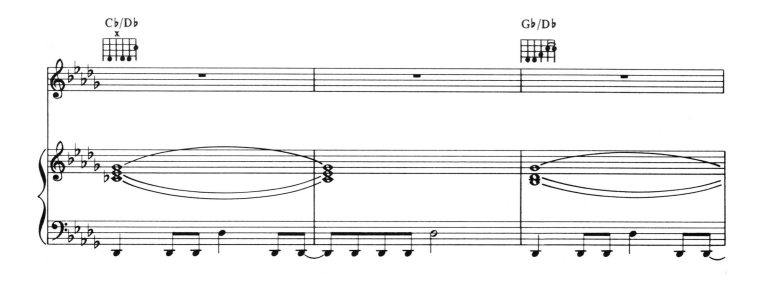

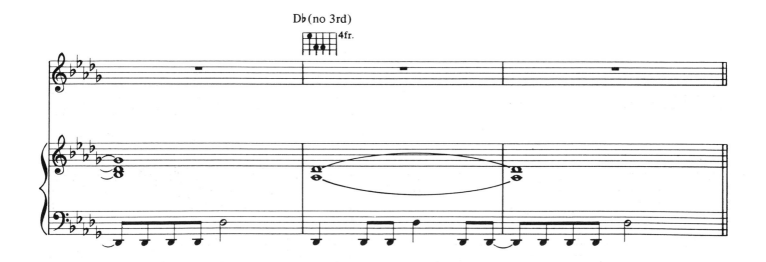

39

When Tomorrow Comes

WORDS & MUSIC BY A. LENNOX, D.A. STEWART & PATRICK SEYMOUR

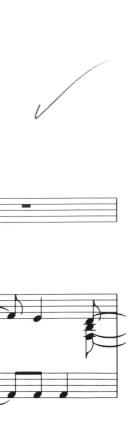

Un - der - neath your dream ___ lit eyes ___
night while you were ly - ing in ___ my arms, ___

an - oth - er day, ___ an - oth - er night ___ has tak - en you ___
and we were feel - ing ve - ry small ___ un - der - neath ___

___ ag - ain my dear, ___ and you know ___ that I'm
___ the un - i - verse, ___

gon - na be ___ the one ___ who'll be ___ there. ___ When you need ___

___ some - one ___ to de - pend up - on, ___ when to - mor - row comes. ___

Sex Crime (1984)

WORDS & MUSIC BY A. LENNOX & D.A. STEWART

Can I___ take this for grant-ed, with your eyes ov-er me.___
And so___ I face the wall___ turn my back a-gainst___ it all.___

In this place___this wint'ry home,___ I know there's al-ways some-one in.___
How I wish___I'd been un-born,___ wish I was un-liv-ing here.___ } Sex
Leave a big___hole in the wall,___ just where you are look-ing in.___

You Have Placed A Chill In My Heart

WORDS & MUSIC BY A. LENNOX & D.A. STEWART

Ah

Ooh

You have placed a chill in my heart.

Thorn In My Side

WORDS & MUSIC BY A. LENNOX & D.A. STEWART

(spoken): You gave me such a bad time, tried to hurt me, but now I know.

Thorn in my side, ___ you know that's all ___ you ev - er were. ___
Thorn in my side, ___ you know that's all ___ you'll ev - er be. ___

___ A bun - dle of lies, ___ you know that's all _
___ So don't think you know bet - ter 'cause that's what _

that it ___ was worth. ___ I should have known ___
you mean to me. ___ I was feel - ing

bet - ter but I trust - ed you ___ at first. ___
com - pli - cat - ed, I was feel - ing low. ___

I should have known bet - ter, but I got what I ___ de-served. _
Now ev - 'ry time I think of you I shi - ver to the bone. _

Ooh Ooh Ooh Ooh Ooh Ooh Ooh Ooh Ooh Ooh Ooh Ooh

Don't Ask Me Why

WORDS & MUSIC BY D.A. STEWART & A. LENNOX

Miracle Of Love

WORDS & MUSIC BY A. LENNOX & D.A. STEWART

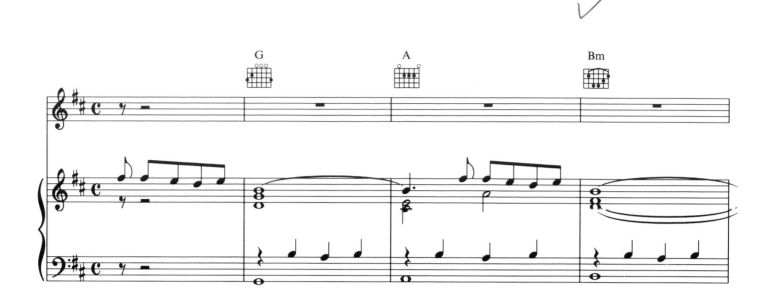

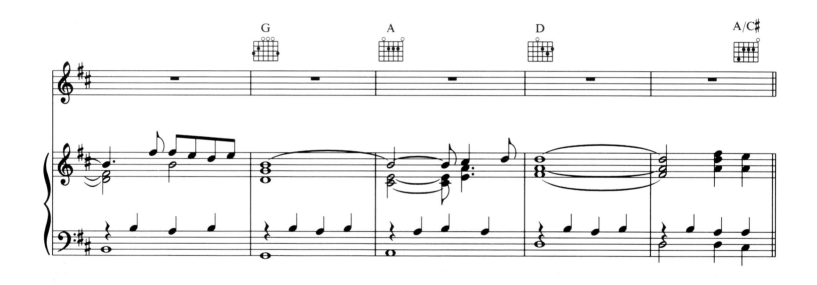

How ma-ny sor-rows____

Cruel is the night that cov-ers up your fears,

do you try ___ to hide ___
ten - der is the one that wipes a - way your tears ___

in a world of il - lu - sion
there must be a bit - ter breeze to make you sting so vic - ious - ly, they

that's cov - er - ing ___ your mind?
say the great-est cow - ard can hurt the most fer - o - cious - ly.

I'll show you
But I'll show you

some-thing good, ___ oh I'll show you some-thing good ___ when you
some-thing good, ___ oh I'll show you some-thing good ___ if you

op - en your mind you'll dis - cov - er the sign that there's
op - en your heart you can make a new start when your

some-thing you're long - ing to find, } the mir - a - cle of love
crum - bl - ing world falls a - part. }

will take a - way your pain, when the mir - a - cle of

love comes___ your way a - gain.

Missionary Man

Words & Music by A. Lennox & D.A. Stewart

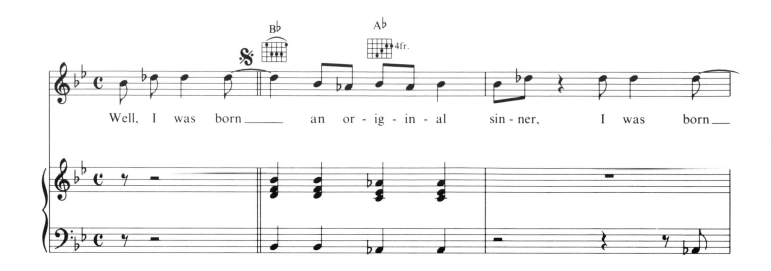

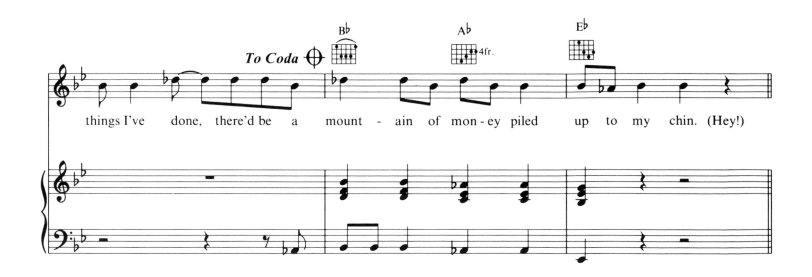

My moth-er told me good, ___ my moth-er told me strong, ___ she said be true to your-self and you can't go wrong, ___ but there's

just one thing ___ that you must un - der - stand, ___ you can

fool with your bro - ther but don't mess with a

mis - sion - a - ry man, don't mess with a mis - sion - a - ry man,

don't mess with a mis - sion - a - ry man,

I Need A Man

WORDS & MUSIC BY A. LENNOX & D.A. STEWART

I don't need a heart break-er, fif-ty faced troub-le-mak-er, two tim-ing time tak-er,

dir-ty lit-tle mon-ey-mak-er, mus-cle bound cheap skate, low down wo-man ha-ter,

tri-ple cros-sing, dou-ble da-ter, yel-la bel-lied al-li-ga-tor.

D.%. al Coda   **CODA**   *ad lib. to fade*

16129 9/93